Alex V
FOR THE LOVE OF ALEX

PENGUIN BOOKS

PENGUIN BOOKS

Published by the Penguin Group
Penguin Books Ltd, 27 Wrights Lane, London W8 5TZ, England
Penguin Books USA Inc., 375 Hudson Street, New York, New York 10014, USA
Penguin Books Australia Ltd, Ringwood, Victoria, Australia
Penguin Books Canada Ltd, 10 Alcorn Avenue, Toronto, Ontario, Canada M4V 3B2
Penguin Books (NZ) Ltd, 182–190 Wairau Road, Auckland 10, New Zealand

Penguin Books Ltd, Registered Offices: Harmondsworth, Middlesex, England

These cartoon strips first appeared in the *Daily Telegraph*
Published in Penguin Books 1992
1 3 5 7 9 10 8 6 4 2

Additional material by Mark Warren

The moral right of the authors has been asserted

Printed in England by Clays Ltd, St Ives plc

Other cartoon books by the same authors
Alex (Mandarin)   *The Unabashed Alex* (Penguin)
Alex II: Magnum Force (Penguin)   *Alex III: Son of Alex* (Penguin)
Alex IV: The Man with the Golden Handshake (Penguin)

With Mark Warren
Celeb (Corgi)

Alex
PEATTIE + TAYLOR

"MEMO FROM RUPERT STERLING TO CORPORATE FINANCE DEPARTMENT. RE: LIGHTS BEING LEFT ON ALL NIGHT."

"IT SHOULD NOT BE NECESSARY TO REMIND YOU THAT, IN COMMON WITH MOST OF OUR COMPETITORS, THE BANK IS CURRENTLY LOSING MONEY..."

"SOME OF YOU MAY CONSIDER OFFICE LIGHTS A TRIVIAL MATTER, BUT IN TIMES OF ECONOMIC RECESSION EVERY LITTLE BIT HELPS..."

"SO LEAVE THEM BURNING ALL NIGHT. LET'S TRY TO GIVE THE IMPRESSION THAT WE'VE GOT SOME WORK."

Alex PEATTIE + TAYLOR

YOUR FRIEND AHMED YOU MET WHEN FILMING OUT IN KURDISTAN. — DID YOU SEE HIM WHEN HE CAME TO ENGLAND?

YES, BUT INSTEAD OF GOING OUT FOR A MEAL WE HAD A QUIET DRINK AND I'M SENDING A DONATION TO THIS "SKIP LUNCH" APPEAL.

SOUNDS LIKE AN APPROPRIATE GESTURE.

QUITE. DO YOU REALISE: BY DONATING THE PRICE OF ONE BUSINESS LUNCH TO FAMINE RELIEF ONE CAN FEED ABOUT 150 PEOPLE IN KURDISTAN. I DON'T NEED TO TELL YOU WHAT THAT MEANS.

YOU'RE OFF THE HOOK WITH THE OTHER 149 PEOPLE YOU SAID "WE MUST DO LUNCH" TO AS WELL.

EXACTLY.

Alex PEATTIE + TAYLOR

WELL, THAT'S IT, JULES. I'VE SKIPPED LUNCH AND I'VE SENT THE MONEY I WOULD HAVE SPENT TO FAMINE RELIEF.

GOOD FOR YOU.

DENYING MYSELF SOMETHING I NORMALLY TAKE FOR GRANTED AS A JOURNALIST MADE THE ACT OF GIVING MORE SATISFYING SOMEHOW.

I GOT REALLY EMOTIONAL AS I WROTE OUT THE CHEQUE AND THOUGHT OF WHAT I'D SACRIFICED TO FEED THE STARVING.

YOUR JOURNALISTIC PRINCIPLE OF ONLY PAYING FOR LUNCH IF YOU CAN CLAIM IT ON EXPENSES?

YES. IT'S A CAREER FIRST FOR ME, I CAN TELL YOU.

Alex PEATTIE + TAYLOR

I'VE MADE SUCH A FOOL OF MYSELF... THE ACCUSATIONS I MADE AGAINST CRESSIDA THE BABYSITTER.

WHAT ARE YOU TALKING ABOUT?

WHEN HAVING MY EVENING GLASS OF 12-YEAR-OLD MALT I'VE RECENTLY NOTICED THAT THE LEVEL OF THIS OTHER BOTTLE OF WHISKY SEEMED TO HAVE BEEN DIMINISHING.

IT'S ONLY SOME CHEAP RUBBISH SO I DIDN'T SAY ANYTHING BUT IT'S BEEN GOING ON FOR A FEW WEEKS NOW AND SO FINALLY I ACCUSED CRESSIDA...

AND HAD SHE BEEN DRINKING IT?

NO. TO MY SHAME SHE HADN'T.

SHE'D BEEN DRINKING THE MALT AND TOPPING UP THE BOTTLE WITH THIS STUFF. AND I HADN'T NOTICED...

Alex PEATTIE + TAYLOR

OBVIOUSLY THE WHOLE BUSINESS OF PLANNING A TAKEOVER IS HIGHLY SECRET WHICH IS WHY WE EMPLOY CODE NAMES TO REPRESENT THE COMPANIES INVOLVED...

IT IS OF PARAMOUNT IMPORTANCE THAT WHAT THE CODE NAMES REFER TO SHOULD NOT BE GUESSED BY OUTSIDE PARTIES...

AND TO MY INTENSE PERSONAL AND PROFESSIONAL EMBARRASSMENT THIS IS PRECISELY WHAT HAS HAPPENED WITH THE NAMES CHOSEN BY YOU, CLIVE...

WHAT? "TROILUS" AND "CRISEYDE"?

YES. ONE OF THE FINANCIAL P.R. PEOPLE KNEW THAT THEY WERE LOVERS IN CHAUCER.

TRY TO BE MORE OBSCURE IN FUTURE. WHAT WAS THAT OXBRIDGE EDUCATION FOR?

Alex PEATTIE + TAYLOR

HOW LONG IS TOBY ELLIS ON HOLIDAY IN BARBADOS FOR?

TWO MORE WEEKS.

NOTICES

WELL I THINK IT'S JOLLY UNFAIR THE WAY PEOPLE WHO ARE JUST LAZING AROUND READING PAPERBACKS ALL DAY FEEL OBLIGED TO SEND SMUG TRIUMPHANT POSTCARDS...

SAYING WHAT A GOOD TIME THEY'RE HAVING, KNOWING FULL WELL THAT THIS IS THE LAST THING THEIR PANICKED AND PRESSURISED COLLEAGUES ACROSS THE SEAS WISH TO HEAR...

OH, SHUT UP, CLIVE...

TAKE A POSTCARD...TO TOBY ELLIS, C/O BEACH VIEW HOTEL, BARBADOS..."FINALLY GOT OUR FIRST DEAL. TOO BAD YOU MISSED OUT. YOUR PERFORMANCE-RELATED BONUS UP THE SPOUT. LOVE, ALEX"

Alex
PEATTIE + TAYLOR

AS THIS REPORT SAYS, A LOT OF US JOURNALISTS ARE TOTALLY THOUGHTLESS IN THE WAY THEY TRY TO INTERVIEW PEOPLE AFFECTED BY A TRAGEDY.

TAKE DOORSTEPPING FOR INSTANCE. I'VE SEEN HACKS ACTUALLY SHOUTING THROUGH PEOPLE'S LETTERBOXES ASKING IF THEY CAN HAVE A FEW WORDS! I WOULDN'T DREAM OF DOING SUCH A THING.

ME NEITHER.

AS A PROFESSIONAL REPORTER, IF I WAS TO DO SOMETHING LIKE THAT I'D BE STOOPING DOWN TO THE LEVEL OF AN ANIMAL.

YOU'D POP ROUND THE BACK AND SHOUT THROUGH THE CAT FLAP?

ABSOLUTELY. CATCHING THEM OFF GUARD IS HALF THE BATTLE.

Alex PEATTIE + TAYLOR

HUMPHREY AND EDWARD ARE BOTH VERY CONCERNED ABOUT THE EFFECT OF PUBLIC REACTION TO THEIR PAY RISES CAUSING EMBARRASSMENT TO THE GOVERNMENT.

REALLY?

YES. I'VE TOLD THEM NOT TO BE SO SOFT. IT'S A LOT OF FUSS ABOUT NOTHING - WHAT THEY EARN AS HEADS OF PRIVATISED INDUSTRIES.

IN THE END WHAT DOES IT MATTER IF PEOPLE LOOK IN THE PAPER AND FIND SOME CAPTAINS OF INDUSTRY HAVE BEEN AWARDED A FEW EXTRA Ks?

JUST BECAUSE YOUR ONE IS A HEREDITARY BARONETCY, SIR TOBY...

QUITE...THE ONES YOU GET GIVEN IN THE HONOURS LIST AREN'T WORTH TUPPENCE.

Alex PEATTIE + TAYLOR

THAT'S A BIG WODGE OF PAPERS CAME IN THE POST FOR YOU.

IT'S THE NEW CHAIN LETTER THAT'S GOING AROUND.

LOOK. ALL THE LETTERS IN THE CHAIN SO FAR. I'M SUPPOSED TO DUPLICATE IT AND SEND IT ON TO FIVE DIFFERENT FRIENDS, PLUS A LETTER FROM MYSELF. APPARENTLY CONTINUING THE CHAIN BRINGS ONE GOOD FORTUNE.

WELL MAKE SURE ONE BATCH GOES TO HARRY. SINCE HE LEFT HERE TO START HIS OWN CORPORATE FINANCE BOUTIQUE, BUSINESS HASN'T GONE TOO WELL FOR HIM. APPARENTLY HE'S DESPERATE TO FIND SOME WORK.

AND YOU THINK THIS MIGHT BRING HIM LUCK?

NO. BUT I'VE HEARD HE HAS TO DO HIS OWN PHOTOCOPYING.

ER... CAROLINE...

Alex — PEATTIE + TAYLOR

Panel 1: CLIVE! REMEMBER THAT CHAIN LETTER I GOT FROM MICHAEL, MY LAWYER - PROMISING GOOD OR BAD LUCK WITHIN 4 DAYS DEPENDING ON WHETHER I SENT IT ON?

YES.

Panel 2: YOU KNOW I SAID IT WAS TOTALLY UNLIKE HIM TO PASS ON SUCH SUPERSTITIOUS TWADDLE AND I THOUGHT HE MUST BE GOING SOFT?

UH-HUH.

Panel 3: WELL IT'S JUST FOUR DAYS SINCE I RECEIVED THE LETTER IN THE POST AND SOMETHING'S JUST HAPPENED THAT'S MADE ME REVISE MY OPINION ENTIRELY.

WHAT?

Panel 4: HE'S BILLED ME FOR IT. LOOK.

OH. WELL THAT'S ALL RIGHT THEN.

Alex — PEATTIE + TAYLOR

Panel 5: I'VE JUST RECEIVED THIS CHAIN LETTER FROM ALEX MASTERLEY AT MEGABANK. IT BRINGS GOOD LUCK IF IT'S SENT ON WITHIN 4 DAYS.

Panel 6: I THOUGHT IT MIGHT BE A NICE GESTURE TO SEND IT ON TO MARTIN DRAKE AT "THE ECHO".

HMMM... REMEMBER HE'S ONE OF OUR BEST CONTACTS IN THE WORLD OF BUSINESS JOURNALISM.

Panel 7: IS THIS STRICTLY IN KEEPING WITH OUR ROLE AS FINANCIAL P.R. PEOPLE?

SENDING A GOOD-LUCK CHAIN LETTER? I DON'T SEE WHY NOT...

Panel 8: HE ONLY HAS TO COPY IT AND ADD A FEW LINES OF HIS OWN.

THAT'S ALL HE EVER DOES WITH ANYTHING WE SEND HIM ANYWAY.

Alex
PEATTIE + TAYLOR

IT LOOKS LIKE CLIVE IS TELLING OUR HOST ABOUT THE FISH THAT GOT AWAY...

OH YES.

AND OLD HAMISH IS LOOKING RATHER SCEPTICAL. AS THIS STRETCH OF THE RIVER BELONGS TO HIM, HE'S AN OLD HAND AT THIS GAME.

HE'S OBVIOUSLY ACCUSING CLIVE OF LYING...

AND NOW WE SEE CLIVE STRIKE THE TIME-HONOURED FISHERMAN'S POSE...

SHAKE

ABOUT TO BE SUBJECTED TO A FULL BODY SEARCH IN CASE HE'S HIDDEN IT ABOUT HIS PERSON.

...WELL, ANY FISH CAUGHT DOES BELONG TO THE HOST.

HE'S VERY PROUD OF HIS CAR'S BOOT.

Alex — PEATTIE + TAYLOR

Panel 1: LOOK AT THAT GORILLA BEING STROKED AND HAVING HIS FUR SEARCHED FOR INSECTS... THAT'S GOING TO LOOK GREAT ON FILM.

I DON'T KNOW, GREG...

Panel 2: IT'S ALL VERY WELL, BUT TODAY'S SOPHISTICATED T.V. AUDIENCES DEMAND SOMETHING MORE THAN JUST THE SIGHT OF WILD ANIMALS BEHAVING AS NATURE INTENDED...

Panel 3: NOW WHAT WOULD BE GREAT IS IF YOU COULD GAIN HIS CONFIDENCE ENOUGH TO GO OVER AND PICK OUT SOME OF HIS TICKS YOURSELF... YOU KNOW, GROOM HIM FOR THE CAMERA...

HMM... SURE...

Panel 4: WHAT, LIKE PREVENTING HIM LOOKING AT IT WHILE WE'RE FILMING? MAYBE STOP HIS HANDS FROM TWITCHING ABOUT...?

ER... TICKS, GREG. ..NOT TICS...

Alex — PEATTIE + TAYLOR

Panel 5: GREG, WHATEVER YOU DO, WHEN ENCOUNTERING THE MALE GORILLA DON'T STARE DIRECTLY INTO HIS EYES. PRETEND TO BE LOOKING AT THE GROUND OR SOMEWHERE ELSE.

WHAT? NOT LOOK AT HIM? HOW?

Panel 6: THIS IS BASIC ROLE-PLAYING, GREG. FORGET SPECIES, IT'S A QUESTION OF DISPLAYING SOCIAL BEHAVIOUR AT A VERY PRIMAL LEVEL... YOU CAN DO THIS, GREG.

BUT WHAT IF HE COMES RIGHT UP TO ME?

Panel 7: LOOK. HE'S BEEN LIVING IN THE JUNGLE ALL HIS LIFE. HE'S NEVER MET ANOTHER HUMAN BEING BEFORE, LET ALONE ANYONE FROM THE CIVILISED WORLD OR THE MEDIA.

UH-HUH...

Panel 8: SO PRETEND HE'S TRYING TO NETWORK WITH YOU AT A PARTY.

OOH-ER... RIGHT. GOT YOU...

Alex
PEATTIE + TAYLOR

AH... LOOK AT HER STRETCHING OUT HER ARMS TOWARDS US AND PURSING HER LIPS... SHE LOOKS LIKE SHE WANTS TO KISS US.

YES. MANY OF OUR CUSTOMS HAVE THEIR ROOTS IN THIS PRIMITIVE BEHAVIOUR.

BUT REMEMBER: WE HAVE EVOLVED ADVANCED SYSTEMS AND GESTURES OF AFFECTION AND GREETING SINCE THIS SORT OF DISPLAY...

AND IT'S LIKELY THAT SHE INTENDS SOMETHING ENTIRELY DIFFERENT FROM WHAT WE WOULD EXPECT WHEN SHE MAKES THIS FACIAL EXPRESSION OF PUCKERING UP HER LIPS LIKE THIS.

LIKE WHAT?

..LIKE ACTUALLY TOUCHING THEM AGAINST OUR MOUTHS OR CHEEKS INSTEAD OF GOING "MWAH" INTO THIN AIR ON EACH SIDE OF OUR HEADS.

OH GAWD. HOW UTTERLY GAUCHE AND PROVINCIAL.

Alex
PEATTIE + TAYLOR

RIGHT, WELL WE'RE ALL PACKED UP AND READY TO GO NOW.

SHH... LOOK AT GREG AND THAT GORILLA FEEDING TOGETHER AS IF IT WERE THE MOST NATURAL THING IN THE WORLD.

I DON'T KNOW WHAT IT TOOK TO GAIN SUCH A LEVEL OF ACCEPTANCE... WAS IT CONFIDENCE?... PERSISTENCE?.. MAYBE JUST STUBBORN OBSTINACY...

BUT YOU'VE GOT TO ADMIRE THE SHEER FORCE OF A PERSONALITY CAPABLE OF BREAKING DOWN THE INSTINCTUAL BARRIERS LIKE THIS...

I MEAN, PINNING AN EXPERIENCED JOURNALIST LIKE GREG DOWN TO A LUNCH DATE ONCE THE FILMING IS OVER... IT'S UNHEARD OF...

YES. I TAKE MY HAT OFF TO THAT SILVERBACK.

Panel 1: These symptoms of yours Penny... I realise this will be dispiriting for you...

It's all right, Doctor...

Panel 2: It's just that all my friends have been constantly asking me when Christopher is going to have a little brother or sister...

I understand...

Panel 3: But I've done all the tests and I'm afraid the results are conclusive...

Panel 4: I'm sorry but you've definitely got a minor ear infection.

This is terrible news.

Panel 5: So how come you're not drinking, Penny?

I'm on antibiotics... I've got an ear infection... honestly...

KNOWING SMILE WINK NUDGE

Panel 6: The increasing number of females in modern business life has given rise to a potent dilemma of etiquette...

Panel 7: Namely, if in business one meets a woman one knows socially, does one kiss her or shake her hand?

Panel 8: On the whole, giving women a peck on the cheek is considered unacceptably patronising and I favour greeting them exactly as one would a man — with a handshake.

Panel 9: A Masonic one?

Precisely. Rub it in that there's still one male institution they're never going to wangle their way into.

Alex PEATTIE + TAYLOR

I NEVER ENJOY THE PROCESS OF SHOWING THE NEW GRADUATE INTAKE ROUND OUR DEPARTMENT.

ME NEITHER...

THOSE YOUNG KNOW-ALLS ALWAYS ASK COMPLEX QUESTIONS ABOUT OUR DATABASE AND ON-LINE SYSTEMS — SHOWING UP OUR TOTAL IGNORANCE OF THE BANK'S INFORMATION TECHNOLOGY.

THESE YOUNG HIGHLY COMPUTER-LITERATE INDIVIDUALS, FAMILIAR WITH ALL THE LATEST SOFTWARE FACILITIES CAN'T FIGURE OUT WHY PEOPLE LIKE US PREFER TO RETAIN AN ILL-ORGANISED MANUAL FILING SYSTEM.

UNTIL WE TAKE OUR REVENGE BY AWARDING THEM THE DULL AND FRUSTRATING TASK OF SORTING IT OUT...

Alex PEATTIE + TAYLOR

HONESTLY. I'M SO SICK OF HEARING SIMMS GO ON ABOUT THE AMOUNT OF WORK HE'S PUT INTO THIS REPORT HE'S WRITING FOR US...

YOUTHFUL EXUBERANCE IS FORGIVABLE IN A GRADUATE, CLIVE

HE'S TALKING ABOUT IT AS IF IT WERE HIS THESIS... IT'S ONLY SOME CRUMMY PROJECT WE'VE GIVEN HIM TO DO TO GET HIM OUT OF OUR HAIR IN HIS FIRST WEEK AT THE BANK.

NO-ONE GIVES A DAMN ABOUT HIM OR HIS REPORT. NO-ONE'S EVEN GOING TO BOTHER TO READ IT.

JUST TRY TO IGNORE HIM.

...HONESTLY, I'VE HARDLY OPENED A BOOK AND I HAVE TO HAND IT IN TOMORROW...

BESIDES, WE'VE ALL SEEN HIM SWOTTING IN THE LIBRARY....

Alex
PEATTIE + TAYLOR

ONE IS ALWAYS TEMPTED TO ASSIGN THE NEW GRADUATES TO THE PETTY CHORES LIKE MAKING COFFEE, FETCHING SANDWICHES, AND TIDYING OUR DESKS...

BUT ONE SHOULD BEAR IN MIND THAT THESE YOUNG PEOPLE HAVE COME FRESH FROM UNIVERSITY AND IT'S BAD PSYCHOLOGY TO START BY GIVING THEM MINDLESS TASKS WHICH THEY'LL ONLY DO SLOPPILY AND UNWILLINGLY...

I AGREE TOTALLY.

ONE REAPS THE BENEFITS FAR MORE IF ON THEIR FIRST DAY ONE SETS THEM SOME ACADEMICALLY CHALLENGING WORK LIKE WRITING A REPORT...

QUITE...

A WEEK LATER, WITH THE DEADLINE APPROACHING THEY'LL DO ANYTHING TO AVOID GETTING DOWN TO IT..

YOUR SANDWICHES, ALEX..

THANKS, ELLIS...ER... I THINK MY PENCIL NEEDS SHARPENING...

Alex
PEATTIE + TAYLOR

GIFTS GIFTS GIFTS GIFTS GIFTS

LONDON SOUVENIRS

CLIVE SEEMS UNHAPPY, ALEX.

I THINK IT'S THOSE SOUVENIR T-SHIRTS YOU'RE CONTEMPLATING BUYING FOR YOUR FAMILIES.

YOU SEE, AS AN EX-OXFORD STUDENT WHO IS PROUD OF HIS UNIVERSITY'S EXCLUSIVE REPUTATION, CLIVE OBJECTS TO THE DEBASING EFFECT OF THESE T-SHIRTS BEARING THE UNIVERSITY CREST AND SOLD TO TOURISTS IN THEIR THOUSANDS.

HE FEELS THAT SUCH GARMENTS CAN ENCOURAGE PEOPLE TO FORM A FALSE IMPRESSION OF THE WEARER'S ACADEMIC SCHOOLING.

PLEASE LET ME TAKE THIS THING OFF, ALEX. PEOPLE WILL ASSUME I DIDN'T GO THERE.

SHUT UP AND KEEP MODELLING IT.

Oxford
UNIVERSITY

Alex
PEATTIE + TAYLOR

CLIVE, IT'S BEEN OVER AN HOUR SINCE I RANG TO SAY THE MINI'S BROKEN DOWN. HURRY UP. IT'S NOT SAFE FOR A WOMAN AROUND HERE AT NIGHT.

I'M SORRY, BRIDGET. I'M NOT FAR AWAY... I CAN'T FIND THE ROAD YOU SAY YOU'RE IN, IN THE A-Z.

WELL ASK SOMEONE FOR DIRECTIONS THEN.

LOOKING FOR A GIRL, DEARIE?

YES I AM ACTUALLY. IN A BLACK MINI.

YOU'RE NICKED LOVER BOY.

KINGS CROSS

BRRRMMM

Alex
PEATTIE + TAYLOR

ASSERT-
IVENESS
COURSE
DAY ①

HOTEL

OKAY... THIRTY SECONDS... YOU CAN STOP LOOKING INTO EACH OTHER'S EYES NOW...

NOW, WHEN WE HAVE A GROUP OF PEOPLE COME HERE NEEDFUL OF ASSERTIVENESS TRAINING THIS IS ALWAYS A USEFUL FIRST EXERCISE.

PHEW. THAT WAS A BIT WEIRD...

GETTING USED TO MEETING THE GAZE OF A COURSE PARTICIPANT CAN BE SOMETHING WHICH REALLY NEEDS TO BE PRACTISED BY CERTAIN PEOPLE.

IT FELT SO UNNATURAL...

NAMELY THE HOTEL BAR STAFF.

I MEAN, I JUST INSTINCTIVELY SEEMED TO WANT TO IGNORE HIM TRYING TO CATCH MY EYE....

NEXT!

AHEM...

ZZZZZ...

Alex PEATTIE + TAYLOR

ER... I'M AFRAID RESULTS HAVE BEEN DISAPPOINTING... ER... SO I HOPE YOU'LL ALL BEAR WITH ME... (GULP) THANKYOU...

ASSERTIVENESS COURSE DAY 2

BIP

OKAY. SO THAT WAS A VIDEO OF THE LAST EXERCISE...

IN WHICH CLIVE IN THE ROLE OF COMPANY CHAIRMAN HAD TO BREAK THE NEWS OF POOR COMPANY FIGURES TO THE REST OF YOU PLAYING MEMBERS OF THE BOARD.

NOW THIS IS THE TIME FOR YOU ALL TO MAKE SOME COMMENTS ON HIS PERFORMANCE.

ER... WELL... NOT BAD...

I THOUGHT YOU DID QUITE WELL...

COME ON. YOU DON'T HAVE TO WORRY ABOUT BEING NICE PEOPLE HERE... LET'S STOP PUSSYFOOTING AROUND, OKAY?

OKAY...

LOOK. CANDIDLY, SIR, I THOUGHT YOU HANDLED THAT MOST IMPRESSIVELY...

THANK YOU...

MUCH, MUCH BETTER. AT LEAST YOU MIGHT KEEP YOUR JOB...

Alex PEATTIE + TAYLOR

CLIVE, IN THIS EXERCISE WE TAKE SITUATIONS WHEN WE ARE UNABLE TO STICK TO OUR GUNS WHEN SOMEONE COMES ON THE PHONE AND STARTS TALKING IN AN AGGRESSIVE MANNER.

ASSERTIVENESS COURSE DAY 2

RIGHT.

ALL OF US CAN THINK OF OCCASIONS WHEN WE REMAIN SILENT AND FAIL TO REACT AND FEEL MORE AND MORE UNCOMFORTABLE ABOUT IT.

DEFINITELY. YES.

AND THE LONGER WE LEAVE ACTUALLY RESPONDING, THE MORE SPINELESS WE APPEAR... NOW I WANT YOU TO RE-ENACT SUCH A SITUATION AND PRACTISE NOT BEING INTIMIDATED BY VERBAL BULLYING...

OKAY.

COME ON, CLIVE... PICK UP THE PHONE... I KNOW YOU'RE THERE... JUST PICK UP THE PHONE...

DON'T DO IT, CLIVE... LEAVE IT.

I CAN'T... I CAN'T...

ANSAFONE

Alex
PEATTIE + TAYLOR

HOTEL

WELL, THERE THEY GO.

THOUGH, IT'S ONLY AFTER A COURSE LIKE THIS IS OVER THAT ONE FINDS OUT IF IT'S HAD ANY EFFECT...

DID WE SUCCESSFULLY INSTILL IN THEM THE QUIET SENSE OF SELF-ASSURANCE AND SELF-BELIEF WHICH WILL ENABLE THEM TO SEE THROUGH ANY COURSE OF ACTION THEY EMBARK UPON?

22

HAVE WE MANAGED TO RID THEM OF THAT PETTY INDECISIVE SPIRIT OF COMPROMISE, HALF-MEASURE AND FEARFULNESS OF THE JUDGEMENT OF OTHERS...?

WE SHALL SOON SEE...

EXCELLENT. ROBIN'S TOTALLY CLEARED OUT HIS ROOM OF SHAMPOO SACHETS, TUBES OF SHOWER GEL AND COMPLIMENTARY SHOWER CAPS. GOOD MAN.

CLIVE'S LEFT A TOKEN FEW BEHIND. I KNEW HE WAS A HOPELESS CASE...

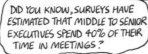

Alex PEATTIE + TAYLOR

THIS IS IT, ALEX. THE PLANE'S GOING DOWN. WE'RE GONERS...

YOU KNOW THEY SAY THAT AS YOU ARE ABOUT TO DIE EVENTS FROM YOUR LIFE FLASH BEFORE YOU...

LITTLE SEEMINGLY TRIVIAL THINGS YOU'D GIVEN NO THOUGHT TO FOR YEARS SUDDENLY REAPPEAR IN FULL CLARITY.

LIKE HOPEFULLY THE SAFETY PROCEDURE DEMONSTRATION. WHERE ARE THE LIFE JACKETS KEPT?

Alex PEATTIE + TAYLOR

OH MY GOD OH MY GOD THE PLANE'S GOING DOWN WE'RE DOOMED.

NO SMOKING FASTEN SEAT BELTS

FLASH   FLASH

STOP PANICKING, CLIVE AND FASTEN YOUR SEAT BELT LIKE THE SIGN SAYS.

WHAT'S THE POINT? WHEN WE IMPACT FROM 30,000 FEET NO-ONE CAN POSSIBLY SURVIVE...

IN A FEW MOMENTS TIME WE'LL BE SCATTERED ACROSS HALF OF BRAZIL IN A TANGLED MESS OF WRECKAGE AND DEAD BODIES...

YES, CLIVE, BUT AT LEAST MINE WILL BE FOUND STRAPPED INTO A FIRST CLASS SEAT.

Alex — PEATTIE + TAYLOR

WOW. LOOK AT THIS. HOW SPOOKY.

YES. APPARENTLY THERE ARE LOST CITIES LIKE THIS DOTTED ALL OVER THE CONTINENT, CUT OFF FROM CIVILIZATION, FORGOTTEN AND DESERTED...

IT PUTS ME IN MIND OF THOSE PERSISTENT LEGENDS OF A SUPPOSED FABULOUS CITY PARADISE WHICH PEOPLE IMAGINED WAS AWAITING DISCOVERY IN TIMES GONE BY...

WHO KNOWS HOW MANY PEOPLE SET OFF INTO THE MIDDLE OF NOWHERE ON HOPELESS QUESTS TO FIND THEIR FORTUNES AND PERISHED ON THE WAY FINDING IT WAS ALL AN ILLUSION...

EL DORADO?

NO THE DOCKLANDS PROPERTY BOOM.

Alex — PEATTIE + TAYLOR

WE'VE GOT TO LIGHT A FIRE AND ATTRACT ATTENTION. LET'S COLLECT SOME BUSHES AND STUFF.

BE CAREFUL OF WHAT YOU DISTURB ROUND HERE, CLIVE. YOU HAVE TO BE AWARE OF THE PROBLEMS INDIGENOUS TO THE RAINFOREST.

CRACK

SOME PLANTS HERE ARE RARE AND HAVE UNKNOWN PROPERTIES...PICK THE WRONG ONE AND THE INDIANS SAY YOU RUN THE RISK OF BEING ON THE RECEIVING END OF A VERY SERIOUS AND SLEEP-INDUCING STING.

SHH... LOOK, HE'S PROBABLY HERE PROMOTING ANOTHER ALBUM.

ERK. THAT WAS A CLOSE ONE.

Alex PEATTIE + TAYLOR

So people have actually survived by cannibalism?

Certainly, Clive. And on some Pacific islands human flesh or "Long Pig" is a great delicacy...

Apparently its taste is something between chicken and pork.

Eurgh...

It is said that we westerners—regardless of cigarette intake—always have a distinctive "smoky bacon" flavour.

Yuk.

Not that I'd ever wish to be experienced about such matters.

Eurgh... Me neither.

I mean, I ABHOR crisps.

Quite. Bar snacks are ghastly plebby things.

Alex PEATTIE + TAYLOR

One sees pictures in the newspapers but it hardly prepares one for a visit to the rainforest.

The sheer brutality of the devastation that's been brought on the Yanomami Indians' heads.

It's obscene the uses to which the Amazon basin has been put.

...creating these haircuts.

Yuk.

Alex PEATTIE + TAYLOR

I MUST SAY THIS INDIAN VILLAGE IS REMARKABLY CIVILISED COMPARED TO WHAT I'D EXPECTED...

I HAD A MENTAL PICTURE OF SOME GOD-FORSAKEN HOLE POPULATED BY THE MOST PRIMITIVE AND FEEBLE-MINDED PEOPLE IMAGINABLE- TOTALLY LACKING IN DIGNITY...

JUST AN UNTHINKING ASSUMPTION I'D MADE THANKS TO THE MISLEADING WAY THE INDIANS' LIVING CONDITIONS ARE DESCRIBED IN THE WEST...

AS "SETTLEMENTS"?

YES, I'D ENVISAGED SOME GHASTLY BACK-OFFICE FULL OF OIKS DOING THE PAPERWORK.

Alex PEATTIE + TAYLOR

IT'S MARVELLOUS HOW THE INDIANS STILL EXIST IN A STATE OF UNSULLIED INNOCENCE..

BUT WHAT ABOUT THIS PORTABLE TELEPHONE THEY'VE BEEN GIVEN BY THE RAINFOREST TRUST SO THEY CAN WARN THEM WHEN ILLEGAL LOGGING TAKES PLACE?

YES, BUT THEIR SOCIETY HASN'T BEEN CORRUPTED BY MODERN ATTITUDES. HERE I STILL FEEL ABLE TO BEHAVE IN A TOTALLY INSTINCTIVE UNINHIBITED WAY WHICH I COULD NEVER DO BACK HOME.

..AND CALL US A HELICOPTER ON THIS THING.

WHERE WE LIVE IT'S TOTALLY NAFF TO BE SEEN USING ONE THESE DAYS...

REACH

WHISPER WHISPER

I EXPECT HE'S TALKING TO A HEADHUNTER

Alex
PEATTIE + TAYLOR

BRITISH CONSULATE

I KNOW THERE ARE BOUND TO BE SOME RETROSPECTIVE RECRIMINATIONS ABOUT THE ACTIONS I SAW FIT TO TAKE IN THE JUNGLE...

THERE ARE DECISIONS YOU HAVE TO TAKE OUT THERE WHICH YOU KNOW YOU'LL FEEL ASHAMED OF WHEN YOU ARE BACK IN CIVILIZED SOCIETY.

S.A.S. GUIDE

WHEN ONE HAS ONLY A COPY OF THE S.A.S. SURVIVAL GUIDE ONE DOESN'T STOP TO QUESTION THE DESIRABILITY OF MAKING USE OF THE PRESERVATION TECHNIQUES IT AFFORDS.

S.A.S. GUIDE

YES, BUT USING IT TO PRESS WILD ORCHIDS? A BIT WET SURELY...

THEY LOOKED SO PRETTY.

Alex PEATTIE + TAYLOR

HI, I'M RORY FROM THE FUTURES DESK. I'M GAY BY THE WAY. I HOPE YOU DON'T MIND ME TALKING TO YOU.

ER... NO. HELLO, MY NAME'S LEWIS, I'M IN ARBITRAGE.

THESE BANK PARTIES! IT'S EASY FOR A BLOKE WHO WANTS TO CHAT UP A SECRETARY HE DOESN'T KNOW.. BUT IT'S MUCH HARDER WHEN HE'S INTERESTED IN ANOTHER MAN...

ER... I SUPPOSE IT IS...

WITH 2 GUYS THERE'S ALL THIS ANXIETY ABOUT SELF-EXPOSURE AND STIGMA BUT I BELIEVE IN BEING TOTALLY OPEN AND GETTING THE INEVITABLE AWKWARD QUESTION OUT OF THE WAY...

DO YOU?

YES... SO:- ARE YOU?.... ERM...YOU KNOW...

BUSY AT THE MOMENT? NO, WORK'S BEEN REALLY QUIET FOR AGES...

PHEW! SAME HERE. IT'S SO EMBARRASSING HAVING TO TALK SHOP.

LOOK: FANCY GOING CLUBBING LATER?

Alex PEATTIE + TAYLOR

PENNY, WE'D BETTER START THINKING ABOUT GETTING CHRISTOPHER HIS XMAS PRESENT.

ALL RIGHT... I'LL TRY THE YELLOW PAGES.

JUST IMAGINE HIS EXCITED LITTLE FACE ON CHRISTMAS MORNING WHEN HIS DREAM COMES TRUE.

ISN'T HE A BIT YOUNG TO APPRECIATE SOMETHING LIKE THIS?

I MEAN, ARE YOU SURE IT'S WHAT HE WANTS?

OH YES. HE TOLD ME HIMSELF HE WANTED A BIKE FOR HIS CHRISTMAS PRESENT.

HERE YOU ARE... "MOTORCYCLE COURIER COMPANIES"

AND WE'LL TELL HIM WE HAD HIS TRAIN SET PICKED UP FROM LAPLAND.

Alex PEATTIE + TAYLOR

ALEX, WHAT'S UP WITH YOU?

THE ONE THING I NEVER ANTICIPATED... I'VE BECOME INFATUATED WITH WENDY MY SECRETARY... WHAT AN IMPOSSIBLE POSITION TO BE IN...

OBVIOUSLY, HAVING HER WORKING AS MY SECRETARY WHEN ALL I'M THINKING OF IS WANTING TO GO OUT WITH HER IS PLAYING HAVOC WITH MY NORMAL FUNCTIONING HERE.

OH DEAR.

WHY DON'T YOU ASK HER OUT?

CLIVE! HOW COULD YOU? I'M A RESPONSIBLE SENIOR EXECUTIVE. I WOULD NEVER ABUSE MY POSITION LIKE THAT.

IT'S NO GOOD. I'LL JUST HAVE TO GET PERSONNEL TO SEND UP ANOTHER SECRETARY FOR ME.

RIGHT SHARON. PHONE UP WENDY ON LINE 3, WOULD YOU, AND ARRANGE A DINNER ENGAGEMENT FOR ME WITH HER THIS WEEK. SHE HAS ALL MY APPOINTMENTS...

Alex PEATTIE + TAYLOR

TAKE MY ADVICE, WENDY, PUT THIS IN YOUR BAG AS WELL.

ARE YOU SERIOUS?

LOOK, YOU NEVER KNOW HOW YOUR FIRST DATE WITH A NEW MAN WILL END. THIS IS THE 90'S. YOU'VE GOT TO BE SAFE.

BUT WE HARDLY KNOW EACH OTHER... ANYWAY ALEX IS SUCH A GENTLEMAN.

AFTER YOU'VE BOTH HAD A BIG DINNER AND A LOT TO DRINK, WENDY, YOU CAN'T TELL WHAT MIGHT HAPPEN... AND THESE DAYS YOU CAN'T TAKE ANYONE FOR GRANTED...

HE MIGHT WANT TO SPLIT THE BILL FIFTY - FIFTY.

I SUPPOSE I'LL NEED MY CHEQUE CARD AS WELL...

Alex PEATTIE + TAYLOR

SHALL WE HAVE ANOTHER BOTTLE OF WINE, WENDY?

OH ALEX. I'M COMPLETELY DRUNK ALREADY...

I HOPE I CAN TRUST YOU. YOU ARE A GENTLEMAN AREN'T YOU? YOU HAVE GOT PRINCIPLES?

WELL, YES, OF COURSE, WENDY...

I MEAN, THERE ARE A LOT OF MEN WHO, WITH A YOUNG, INEXPERIENCED GIRL WHO'S HAD TOO MUCH TO DRINK, MIGHT BE TEMPTED TO TAKE ADVANTAGE OF THE SITUATION...

NO. NOT ME, WENDY. IT WOULD BE BENEATH ME.

I WOULDN'T DREAM OF ORDERING CHEAP PLONK ONCE YOU WERE PAST NOTICING... AND ANYWAY I'M GOING TO BILL ALL THIS TO CLIENTS.

CLICK

Alex PEATTIE + TAYLOR

SO YOU'RE THINKING OF GETTING RID OF YOUR PERSONALISED NUMBER PLATES, ALEX?

THESE DAYS I FIND MYSELF CONTEMPTUOUS OF PEOPLE WHO STILL HAVE THEM, CLIVE.

OBVIOUSLY THEY WERE DE RIGUEUR BACK IN THE BOOM DAYS OF THE 80s WHEN JUST ABOUT EVERYONE WAS DRIVING A FLASH NEW BMW OR PORSCHE.

BUT WITH THE RECENT MOOD OF AUSTERITY IN THE CITY THEY SEEM FALSE AND HOLLOW... NO, I CAN SEE WHEN IT'S TIME TO GET MYSELF A NORMAL ANONYMOUS REGISTRATION PLATE.

THIS AUTUMN. WHICH WILL PROVE THAT I'M DRIVING THIS YEAR'S MODEL. SOME OF THESE PEOPLE HAVEN'T HAD THEIR COMPANY CARS REPLACED FOR 3 OR 4 YEARS, YOU KNOW.

OH. I SEE.

Alex PEATTIE + TAYLOR

WELL I NEVER. FANCY GILES FROM METROBANK GIVING UP SMOKING FOLLOWING A DEPARTMENTAL BAN.

HE USED TO BE A 60-A-DAY MAN.

WITH THIS ANTI-SMOKING CAMPAIGN ATTENTION HAS REALLY BECOME FOCUSSED ON PEOPLE'S WORKING ENVIRONMENTS.

I'LL SAY.

MEASURES LIKE THESE, AT WORK, MAKE ONE AWARE THAT IF SOMEONE LIKE GILES SMOKES IT AFFECTS NOT ONLY HIMSELF BUT THOSE AROUND HIM AS WELL.

ONE CAN'T IGNORE THE MESSAGE CAN ONE?

NO... I ALWAYS THOUGHT HE HAD HIS OWN OFFICE...

EXACTLY... WHAT AN EYE OPENER.

Alex PEATTIE + TAYLOR

LABOUR APPEAR TO BE MOUNTING A CREDIBLE CHALLENGE THIS TIME.

ELECTION MAIN PARTIES NECK AND NECK

THAT'S BECAUSE TRADITIONAL TORY VOTERS LIKE OURSELVES HAVE BEEN BADLY MISREPRESENTED, CLIVE.

IT'S OUR OWN FAULT. WE'VE BEEN GUILTY OF HIGH-HANDED COMPLACENCY, TENDING TO BECOME ENTRENCHED IN OUR DEMANDING BUSINESS SCHEDULES AND ELITIST LIFESTYLES.

BUT WE NEED TO BE LESS DISMISSIVE OF PEOPLE WE THINK OF AS OUR SOCIAL INFERIORS, RECOGNISE THE IMPORTANCE OF THE MAN OR WOMAN IN THE STREET.

WHAT, OPINION POLLSTERS?

YES, NEXT TIME WE SPY ONE OF THOSE GROTTY CLIP-BOARD CHAPPIES WE'D BETTER DEIGN TO SPEAK TO THEM.

Alex PEATTIE + TAYLOR

OH DEAR. LOOK AT THIS MOUNTAIN OF WORK THAT STILL NEEDS DOING. I'M AFRAID I'M GOING TO HAVE TO BREAK OUR DATE TONIGHT, WENDY.

OH NO, ALEX. IT'S NOT FAIR.

LOOK, WENDY, I KNOW YOU'RE UPSET BUT THIS IS GOING TO HAPPEN FROM TIME TO TIME WHEN AN IMPORTANT JOB COMES UP...

I'M SORRY BUT THIS IS AN UNUSUAL CIRCUMSTANCE WE FIND OURSELVES IN... AND THIS IS ONE THING YOU'LL HAVE TO LEARN TO ACCEPT IF WE'RE GOING TO BE DATING EACH OTHER...

THAT I CAN ALWAYS MAKE SURE YOU'RE FREE TO WORK LATE AND FINISH THINGS OFF...I'LL CALL YOU FROM THE PUB LATER AND SEE HOW YOU'RE GETTING ON.

Alex
PEATTIE + TAYLOR

Panel 1: AS MY SECOND YOU ARE THE ONLY PERSON WHO KNOWS ABOUT THIS DUEL I'M FIGHTING THIS MORNING, CLIVE.

Panel 2: BUT I'VE PLACED A LETTER IN MY POCKET EXPLAINING THE WHOLE SITUATION - TO BE OPENED ONLY IN THE EVENT OF MY BEING KILLED.

Panel 3: I STOLE OFF SILENTLY THIS MORNING, TELLING NO-ONE WHERE I WAS GOING... IF I DIE THERE'LL BE A LOT OF TALK AND I'D PREFER PEOPLE TO KNOW IT HAPPENED WHILE I WAS EMBARKED UPON AN HONOURABLE COURSE OF ACTION...

Panel 4: AND NOT WHILE YOU WERE SECRETLY SEEING A HEADHUNTER.

YES. THOUGH I IMAGINE IT IS RARE TO DROP DEAD DURING A BREAKFAST MEETING...

Alex
PEATTIE + TAYLOR

Panel 5: WELL, YOU CERTAINLY MADE MINCEMEAT OF WAYNE IN THAT DUEL.

YES, AS SOON AS I CLAPPED EYES ON HIS CHOICE OF WEAPONS I KNEW MY LUCK WAS IN.

Panel 6: OF COURSE, PART OF MY UPBRINGING AS A GENTLEMAN WAS THE ACQUIRING OF CERTAIN SKILLS WHICH GIVE ME AN ADVANTAGE IN THAT FIELD OF ARMED COMBAT.

Panel 7: IN SPITE OF WAYNE'S LAUGHABLE CLAIMS TO HAVE LEARNED TO FENCE PROFESSIONALLY.

QUITE.

Panel 8: PROFESSIONAL HANDLERS OF STOLEN GOODS WOULD NOT GET FOBBED OFF WITH A PAIR OF REPRODUCTION ANTIQUE DUELLING PISTOLS.

ESPECIALLY ONES WHICH ARE INTENDED TO BE USED AS FIRE LIGHTERS.

Alex
PEATTIE + TAYLOR

ALEX, ARE WE REALLY SUPPOSED TO ACTUALLY GO AND LIVE IN THAT GHASTLY CONSTITUENCY YOU'RE STANDING FOR?

I'M AFRAID SO, PENNY.

REMEMBER I'M CONTESTING THE SAFEST LABOUR SEAT IN THE LAND. PEOPLE IN THE AREA ARE TRADITIONALLY DEEPLY HOSTILE TO TORY CANDIDATES...

AND TAKING INTO ACCOUNT THE SEVERE EFFECT OF THE RECESSION I FEEL THAT PURCHASING A HOUSE IN THE CONSTITUENCY WILL MAKE ME MORE ACCEPTABLE TO THE LOCAL ELECTORATE.

A BUYER? PLEASE COME IN.

PERHAPS I COULD FIRST ASK YOU ABOUT YOUR VOTING INTENTIONS...

DOBBS FOR SALE

FOR SALE

FOR SALE

FOR SALE

I DON'T WANT TO LOOK LIKE A TOWNIE.

VOTE TORY

Alex
PEATTIE + TAYLOR

FRANKLY, VANORA, SOME OF THE PARTY WORKERS ARE A BIT SCEPTICAL ABOUT HAVING A WELL-KNOWN ACTRESS AS OUR LABOUR CANDIDATE.

OBVIOUSLY YOU'RE A NATURAL FOR CANVASSING, BEING ACCUSTOMED TO PERFORMING IN PUBLIC... AND YOUR PERSONAL POPULARITY GIVES US A GREAT EDGE OVER THE OTHER PARTIES.

BUT, JUST SAY YOU DO WIN. WHAT PEOPLE WANT TO KNOW IS WILL YOU BE ABLE TO HANDLE WHAT COMES NEXT?

OH YES...

...STAND UP, LOOKING BEWILDERED AS IF IT WAS A COMPLETE SURPRISE AND PRETEND NOT TO HAVE PREPARED AN ACCEPTANCE SPEECH...

ER...

Alex
PEATTIE + TAYLOR

Panel 1: WILL YOU BE VOTING IN THIS CONSTITUENCY?

NO. AND NOT NOWHERE ELSE EITHER.

Panel 2: WHAT? I HOPE YOU'RE NOT ONE OF THOSE IRRESPONSIBLE PEOPLE WHO MOVE AREAS WITHOUT BEING ON ANY COUNCIL'S REGISTERS.

Panel 3: BECAUSE IF YOU THINK YOU CAN AVOID PAYING POLL TAX BY NOT BEING ON ANY LOCAL ELECTORAL LIST THEY'LL CATCH YOU IN THE END YOU KNOW...

Panel 4: NO, NO... DON'T WORRY...

OH... SO YOU ARE ON A ROLL THEN?

Panel 5: YEP. LONGEST RUN OF LUCK EVER, I RECKON... I HAVEN'T EVEN HAD TO PAY RATES SINCE 1976.

Alex
PEATTIE + TAYLOR

Panel 1: VOTE VANORA HOBSON

VANORA'S GOT ANOTHER INTERVIEW SPOT ON T.V.

WELL LET'S HOPE SHE DOESN'T BLOW IT THIS TIME.

Panel 2: ACTUALLY, IMPRESSIVELY, SHE'S STICKING PRETTY MUCH TO THE RECORD OF THE GOVERNMENT AND CAMPAIGNING ON ISSUES OF POLICY... BUT, OH DEAR... SHE CAN'T RESIST MAKING IT PERSONAL TOO...

OH NO.

Panel 3: OH YES... SHE'S GETTING SOME NASTY DIGS IN AS YOU MIGHT EXPECT...

I WARNED HER: THE PUBLIC DON'T LIKE THIS SORT OF THING...

Panel 4: WELL DARLINGS WHEN I WAS IN REP AT SALFORD I STAYED WITH THIS TYPICAL OLD LANDLADY...

UNFORTUNATELY ALL ACTORS THINK THEIR TEDIOUS THEATRICAL BOARDING-HOUSE STORIES ARE HILARIOUS...

VOTE VANORA HOBSON

SHE WON'T LISTEN WILL SHE?

Alex
PEATTIE + TAYLOR

OI. WHAT ARE YOU DOING KISSING MY BABY LIKE THAT?

HUH?

YOU DON'T IMPRESS ME YOU BIG PHONEY.

LOOK I WAS ACTING IN A PERFECTLY NATURAL WAY...

YOU SMARMY BERK. I'VE SUSSED YOU. YOU'VE BEEN ON ONE OF THOSE TRAINING COURSES WHERE YOU LEARN ADVANCED MEDIA AND P.R. TECHNIQUES HAVEN'T YOU?

WELL YES I HAVE.

...BUT LOTS OF PEOPLE GO "MWAH, MWAH, MWAH" ON EACH SIDE OF SOMEONE'S FACE WITHOUT ACTUALLY TOUCHING THEM THESE DAYS...

GIVE HIM A PROPER KISS OR I'M VOTING LABOUR.

YOU MUST BE JOKING.

Alex
PEATTIE + TAYLOR

WHAT MADE YOU WANT TO BE AN M.P., ALEX?

LAW AND ORDER, CLIVE. AS A FATHER MYSELF I AM INCREASINGLY CONCERNED ABOUT THE KIND OF SOCIETY CHRISTOPHER WILL BE GROWING UP IN.

VOTE CONSERVATIVE

THESE DAYS IT'S SO EASY FOR YOUNG PEOPLE TO BE LURED INTO DRUG AND ALCOHOL ABUSE AND THEN MOVE ON TO FAST CARS AND PETTY MISDEMEANOURS. IT'S NOT SURPRISING SO MANY OF THEM END UP IN TROUBLE WITH THE POLICE.

VOTE CONSERVE

AS AN ELECTED M.P. I BELIEVE I WOULD BE IN A POSITION TO DO SOMETHING ABOUT IT BEFORE IT'S TOO LATE.

VOTE CONSER

NAMELY PULL A FEW STRINGS AND GET HIM LET OFF?

IT'S ONE OF THE PERKS OF THE JOB, CLIVE.

VOTE CONSE

WAAH

Alex PEATTIE + TAYLOR

LOOK, DOCTOR. IT'S ABOUT THE CASE OF MRS HIGGINS HERE, WHO'S BEEN WAITING 7 MONTHS FOR SURGERY TO TAKE AN ENLARGED.. ER... "BEAUTY SPOT" OFF HER CHIN.

CONSULTANT'S OFFICE

APPARENTLY ONE OF YOUR STAFF HERE CONFIRMED TO THE PAPERS THAT THE DELAY WAS A RESULT OF N.H.S. BUNGLING. ...IT'S ABSOLUTELY SCANDALOUS...YOU MUST BE ABLE TO DO SOMETHING ABOUT THIS.

OH DEAR. YES... YES, OF COURSE..

SHUFFLE

WELL, MRS HIGGINS, I THINK WE SHOULD HAVE THAT MOLE REMOVED IMMEDIATELY.

OH GOOD.

WHO WAS IT? I'LL SACK THE LITTLE SNEAK.

ONE OF THE NURSES APPARENTLY. I THINK YOU'LL FIND SHE VOTES LABOUR.

ER...

Alex PEATTIE + TAYLOR

HOW'S IT GOING?

I'M GETTING A VERY POOR RESPONSE ROUND HERE...IT'S GETTING HARDER AND HARDER TO GET OUR MESSAGE ACROSS ON THESE ESTATES.

THE PEOPLE HAVE BECOME TOTALLY FED UP WITH POLITICIANS COMING ROUND CANVASSING FOR THE ELECTION. MOST OF THEM JUST DON'T WANT TO KNOW...

DON'T GIVE UP, CLIVE... THERE'S ANOTHER PARTY ELECTION BROADCAST TONIGHT FOR THE CONSERVATIVE PARTY.

OH GOOD. THAT USUALLY MAKES OUR JOB A BIT EASIER.

ITS THE ONLY TIME I CAN GET ANYONE TO COME TO THE DOOR.

IT STARTS AT NINE O'CLOCK.

Alex
PEATTIE + TAYLOR

OKAY, PENNY, WE WON'T BOTHER CANVASSING THAT ESTATE... I CAN SEE CLIVE'S CAR PARKED THERE ALREADY...

VOTE TORY

ALEX MASTERLEY

I MIGHT HAVE GUESSED HE'D BE IN THERE FIRST... HE'S ALWAYS PREPARED TO CANVASS EVEN IN THE ROUGHEST AREAS WE SEND HIM.

VOTE TORY

ALEX MASTERLEY

I MUST SAY WHEN YOU'RE ON THE CAMPAIGN TRAIL IN DEPRESSING CIRCUMSTANCES IT REALLY HELPS ONE KEEP GOING SEEING THE EXAMPLE SET BY A PARTY WORKER LIKE CLIVE.

VOTE TORY

HE'S TIRELESS ISN'T HE?

I'M AFRAID SO... ALL FOUR GONE BY THE LOOKS OF THINGS... KEEP GOING... LOOKS LIKE THEY ALL VOTE LABOUR IN THERE...

VOTE TORY

TAXI!